Tips for Reading Together

Children learn best when reading is fun.

- Talk about the title and the pictures on the cover.
- Look through the pictures together and discuss what you think the story might be about.
- Read the story together, inviting your child to read as much of it as they can.
- Give lots of praise as your child reads, and help them when necessary.
- Try different ways of helping if they get stuck on a word. For example, get them to say the first sound of the word, or break it into chunks, or read the whole sentence again, trying to guess the word. Focus on the meaning.
- Have fun finding the hidden letters.
- Re-read the story later, encouraging your child to read as much of it as they can.

Children enjoy re-reading stories and this helps to build their confidence.

Have fun!

Find the letters in the pictures that make up the name
GOLDILOCKS

Hungry Floppy

Written by Roderick Hunt
Illustrated by Alex Brychta

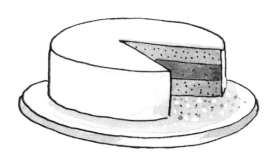

OXFORD
UNIVERSITY PRESS

The family went camping. They
put up a tent.

It took a long time to put up the tent. Floppy was hungry.

Floppy was so hungry, he ran
off to look for food.

A man was cooking.
"That smells good," thought Floppy,
"and I'm so hungry."

"Go away!" called the man.
"You can't have our dinner."
Floppy ran off.

Floppy saw a dog's bowl.
"This smells good," he thought,
"and I'm so hungry."

A big dog barked at Floppy.
"Go away," growled the dog.
"You can't have my dinner."

Floppy was lost. He saw lots
of tents but they all looked
the same to him.

Floppy could smell something.
He sniffed and sniffed. Something
smelled good.

Floppy went inside the tent.
He saw three plates. There was a
slice of cake on each one.

By now, Floppy was *very* hungry.
So he ate the big slice.

He was still hungry, so he ate the
smaller slice.

But Floppy was *still* hungry, so
he ate the very small slice, too.
"I need a rest now," he thought.

There were three beds. Floppy went on the blue bed, but it was too hard.

Then Floppy went on the green
bed, but it was too soft.

In the end, he lay on the red bed. It was not too hard or too soft. It was just right. So he went to sleep.

Soon, a girl came back to the
tent with her mum and dad.
It was Anneena!

"Someone has eaten my cake,"
said Anneena.

"Someone has eaten *all* the cake,"
said Anneena's mum. "And look
who's sleeping on your bed."

"It's Floppy!" said Anneena. "What are you doing here, you naughty dog?"

Anneena and her dad looked
for Biff and Chip. At last, they
found them.

"What a surprise to see you!"
said Biff.

Anneena told them about Floppy.

"Never mind," said Dad. "Stay
and have some of our cake."

Think about the story

Why did Floppy steal the food? Was he wrong to steal it?

Why didn't Floppy go and look for Kipper himself?

How is this story like Goldilocks and the Three Bears?

What would you do if you got lost in a strange place?

Matching pairs

Find pairs of things that start with the same letter.
Which one isn't in the story?